Disney LEARNING

MATH
BRAIN BOOST

GRADE
2

NELSON

This workbook belongs to:

_____

Disney LEARNING

COPYRIGHT © 2018 Disney Enterprises, Inc.
All rights reserved.

Published by Nelson Education Ltd.

ISBN-13: 978-0-17-685501-7
ISBN-10: 0-17-685501-7

Printed and bound in Canada
1 2 3 4   21 20 19 18

For more information contact Nelson Education Ltd.,
1120 Birchmount Road, Toronto, Ontario M1K 5G4.
Or you can visit our website at nelson.com.

For permission to use material from this text or product,
submit all requests online at cengage.com/permissions.
Further questions about permissions can be emailed to
permissionrequest@cengage.com.

Credits: 18-21, 46-49, 113, 114: Coin images © 2018 Royal Canadian Mint.

Contents

Track Your Learning   2

Number   4

Patterns and Algebra   50

Measurement   64

Geometry   80

Data and Probability   92

Answers   100

Learning Tools   112

Completion Certificate   117

Track Your Learning

START

| 1 | 2 | 3 | 4 |

| 24 | 23 | 22 | 21 | 20 |

| 25 | 26 | 27 | 28 | 29 | 30 |

| 46 | 45 | 44 | 43 | 42 |

| 47 | 48 | 49 | 50 |

| 69 | 68 | 67 |

| 70 | 71 | 72 |

Colour a circle for every completed activity
to finish the Brain Boost learning path!

5 6 7 8 9 10 11 12

19 18 17 16 15 14 13

31 32 33 34 35 36

41 40 39 38 37

51 52 53 54 55 56 57 58

66 65 64 63 62 61 60 59

73 74 FINISH

Fill In the Blanks

Officer Clawhauser greets hundreds of visitors every day.

Fill in the missing numbers in the 100-chart.

1	2	3		5	6	7		9	10
11		13	14	15		17	18	19	
21	22		24		26	27	28		30
	32	33	34	35	36		38	39	40
41	42		44	45		47	48	49	
51		53	54	55	56	57		59	60
61	62	63		65	66	67	68		70
71	72		74	75	76	77		79	80
	82	83	84		86		88	89	90
91	92	93		95	96	97	98	99	

Crack the Code

What is Judy's motto about Zootopia?

To find out, skip count by 5s. Then crack the code!

Letter Code

A 5   I 10   N 15   Y _____

O _____   C 30   B _____   H _____

G _____   T 50   E _____   S 60

___ ___ ___ ___ ___ ___
5   15   20   25   15   55

___ ___ ___ ___ ___
30   5   15   35   55

___ ___ ___ ___ ___ ___ ___ ___!
5   15   20   50   40   10   15   45

HINT Use the 100-chart on page 112 in the Learning Tools to help you skip count by 5s.

Connect the Dots

Moana walks into a secret cave. What does she see? Start at 30. Count backward by 1s. Connect the dots.

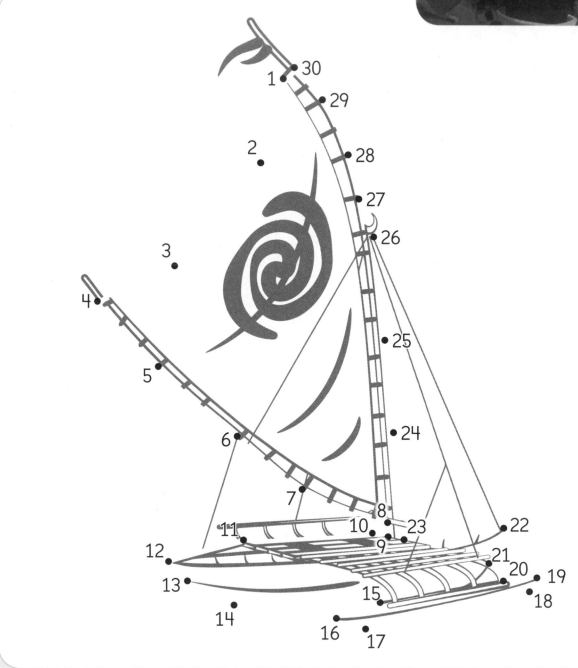

Maze

Moana reads the stars to return the heart to Te Fiti.

Skip count backward by 10s to complete the maze.

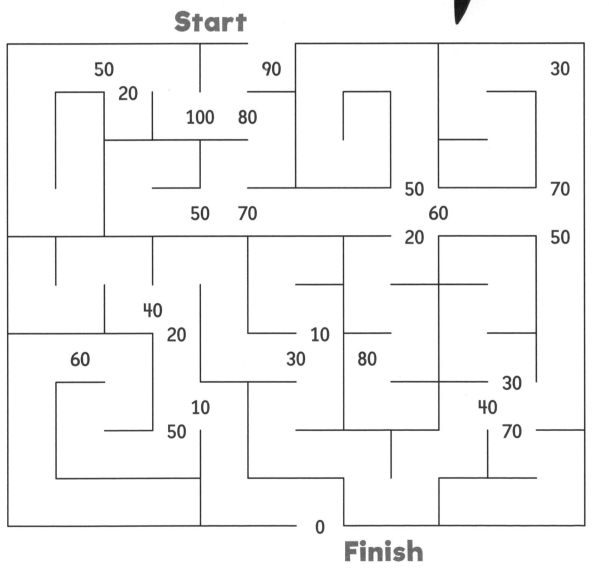

Colour to Complete

Sina and Tui are collecting coconuts.

Show 34 coconuts using these 10-frames.

Show 67 coconuts using these 10-frames.

9

Matching

Thirty-two Kakamora are attacking Moana. Thirty-two can also be shown using the number 32.

Draw a line to match the word to the number.

46   twenty-four

71   fifty-nine

90   eighty-five

24   seventy-one

59   sixty-three

63   thirty-seven

85   forty-six

37   ninety

Picture

Moana returns to Motunui. Base ten blocks can be used to represent the population of villages like Motunui.

Sketch each number using base ten blocks.

22

41

68

99

HINT You can sketch a tens rod like this:▯. You can sketch a ones block like this: ▫.

Fill In the Blanks

Judy takes the train to Zootopia. The train cars are in order by number.

Label the train cars with numbers from the Number Bank. Order these numbers from greatest to least. The first one is done for you.

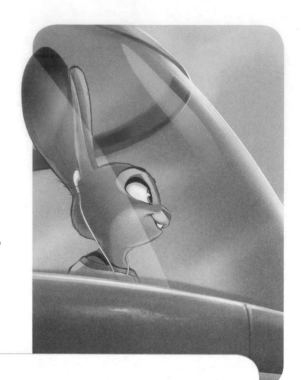

Number Bank

39   56   93   16   65   88

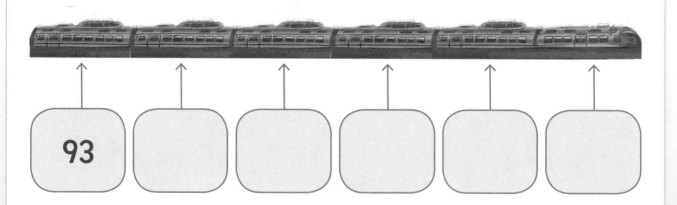

93

Fill In the Blanks

Judy Hopps answers questions from reporters.

Label the badges with numbers from the Number Bank. Order these numbers from least to greatest. The first one is done for you.

Number Bank

54	21	99
12	33	76

12

Colour to Complete

Nick has a cooler full of pawpsicles. He sells them to the lemmings.

Colour the pawpsicle in each set that shows the lesser number.

19 17

32 36

21 20

28 32

89 78

60 65

100 99

55 53

Circling

Judy trains hard. She does each exercise many times.

Circle the greater number in each set.

12	22	sit-ups
28	24	push-ups
63	66	skips
55	75	pull-ups
77	74	jumping jacks
99	91	squats
82	88	chin-ups
44	14	hops
38	39	toe touches
35	53	arm circles

Picture Clues

Little Moana likes to collect shells.
She has 5 shells.

Look at each set of shells. Estimate.
Then count.

Estimate the number of shells below.

There are about _____ shells.

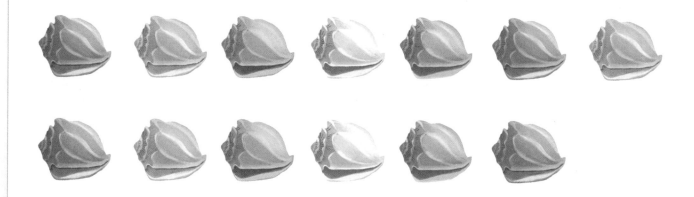

Now count the number of shells.

There are _____ shells.

Estimate: There are about _____
blue shells.

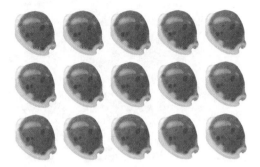

Actual count: There are _____
blue shells.

Estimate: There are about _____
green shells.

Actual count: There are _____
green shells.

Word Search

The lemmings love pawpsicles. They pay Nick. Nick needs to make change.

Identify each coin. (Circle) its name in the word search.

 _____

 _____

 _____

 _____

_____

```
P  Q  U  A  R  T  E  R
B  K  G  N  W  Q  I  O
R  L  O  O  N  I  E  L
I  O  H  R  D  R  B  P
H  K  T  O  O  N  I  E
A  N  I  C  K  E  L  G
W  C  C  J  T  M  J  H
H  I  V  R  D  I  M  E
```

Matching

Nick and Finnick love to make money.
Match each group of coins to how
much it is worth.

                           $1

                           15¢

                           $2

                           25¢

                                               20¢

Fill In the Blanks

All this treasure must be valuable!
Estimate the value of each set of coins. Then count to find the actual value.

1.

   Estimate: There are about _____ cents.

   Actual value: There are _____ cents.

2.

   Estimate: There are about _____ cents.

   Actual value: There are _____ cents.

3.

   Estimate: There are about _____ cents.

   Actual value: There are _____ cents.

Picture Clues

Maui's fishhook is more valuable than all the treasure.

(Circle) the coins in each pair that have a greater value.

Picture

Judy hands out 67 parking tickets an hour!

You can show 67, or any other number, in several ways.

Sketch base ten blocks to represent 67.

Now represent 67 another way.

HINT You can sketch a tens rod like this: ▯. You can sketch a ones block like this: ▫.

Sketch base ten blocks to represent 45.

Now represent 45 in another way.

Sketch base ten blocks to represent 90.

Now represent 90 in another way.

Matching

Gideon Grey bakes pies.

How much pie is left? Match each pie to the correct fraction words.

one fourth

one half

one third

How much of each shape is coloured in? Match each picture to the correct fraction words.

one fourth

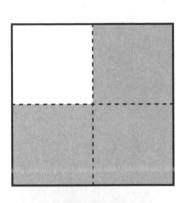

one third

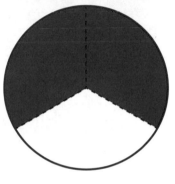

three fourths

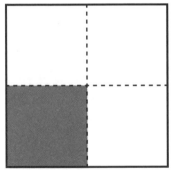

two thirds

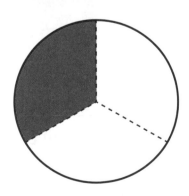

Colour to Complete

When Te Fiti smiles, life blooms again on the island of Motunui.

Colour one fourth of this flower.

Colour one third of this flower.

Colour one half of this flower.

Colour one third of this flower.

Colour one fourth
of the flowers.

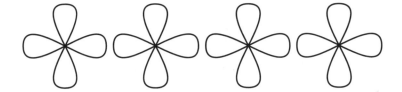

Colour one third
of the flowers.

Colour one half
of the flowers.

Colour one third
of the flowers.

HINT Where there are 4 equal parts, we call each part a
fourth or a quarter. Two quarters equals one half.

27

Crossword

Maui holds one fish. You could use **one** or **1** to represent that number.

Complete the crossword. Write the number word for each number. The first one is done for you.

Across

1. 19
3. 17
5. 14
8. 10
10. 13
11. 16

Down

2. 12
4. 11
6. 20
7. 15
9. 18

¹NINE²TEEN

HINT If you do not have as many letters as squares, check the spelling of your number word.

Function Box

Moana is playing with 1 shell. If she adds 0 shells, she still has 1 shell to play with.

Determine the sum. Then determine the difference.

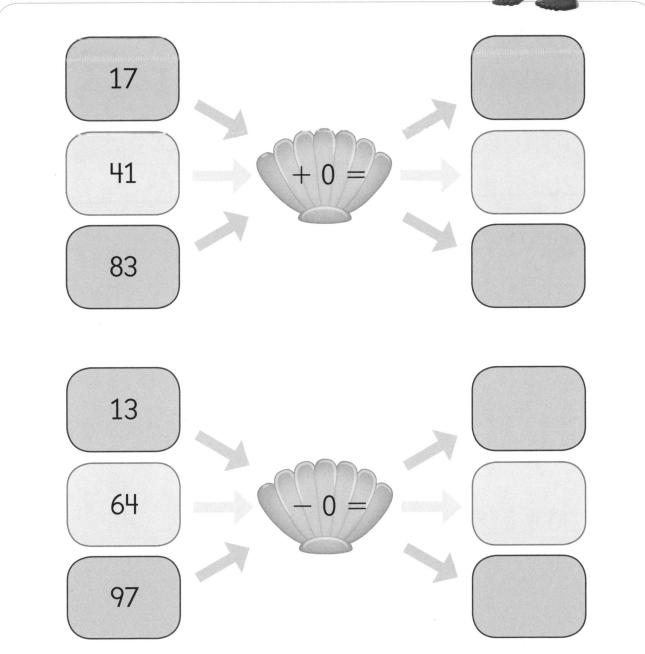

17

41

83

$+ 0 =$

13

64

97

$- 0 =$

Fill In the Blanks

Chief Tui tells Moana about the pile of stones each chief has added to.

Solve the addition sentences. Then write the number word. The first one is done for you.

10 + 10 **20** **twenty**	15 + 15 _____	40 + 40 _____
20 + 20 _____	35 + 35 _____	25 + 25 _____
30 + 30 _____	5 + 5 _____	45 + 45 _____

Picture Clues

Maui is a master fisher. The fish seem to be drawn to his boat.

Count the fish in each set. Write an addition sentence and solve.

_____ + _____ = _____

_____ + _____ = _____

_____ + _____ = _____

HINT Solve each sum by making friendly numbers.
For example, 10 + 11 can be shown as 10 + 10 + 1.

Colour to Complete

Officer Clawhauser loves doughnuts.

Colour the doughnuts. Use the Colour Key.

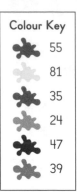

Colour Key	
	55
	81
	35
	24
	47
	39

22 + 2 = _____

30 + 17 = _____

20 + 15 = _____

29 + 10 = _____

25 + 30 = _____

40 + 41 = _____

HINT Use mental math strategies to help you find the sum.

Solve the Riddle

Judy looks for clues to solve a crime.

What has four legs but does not walk? Calculate each sum. Then solve the riddle.

$$\begin{array}{r} 20 \\ +\ 6 \\ \hline \end{array}$$
B

$$\begin{array}{r} 30 \\ +\ 32 \\ \hline \end{array}$$
E

$$\begin{array}{r} 10 \\ +\ 5 \\ \hline \end{array}$$
L

$$\begin{array}{r} 40 \\ +\ 49 \\ \hline \end{array}$$
A

$$\begin{array}{r} 18 \\ +\ 43 \\ \hline \end{array}$$
R

$$\begin{array}{r} 20 \\ +\ 25 \\ \hline \end{array}$$
T

$$\begin{array}{r} 24 \\ +\ 54 \\ \hline \end{array}$$
N

$$\begin{array}{r} 51 \\ +\ 12 \\ \hline \end{array}$$
O

$$\begin{array}{r} 22 \\ +\ 13 \\ \hline \end{array}$$
J

___   ___ ___ ___   ___   ___
89   45   89   26   15   62

HINT Not all the letters are needed to solve the riddle. One letter is used twice.

Fill In the Blanks

Moana uses resources from the land to repair her boat. You can use resources, such as counters, to help you subtract.

Write each subtraction sentence.

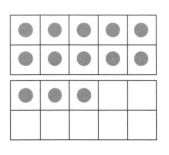 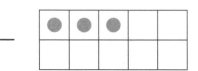

_____ − _____ = _____

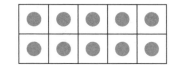

_____ − _____ = _____

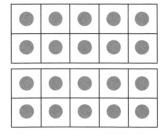 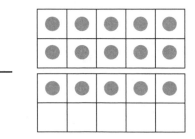

_____ − _____ = _____

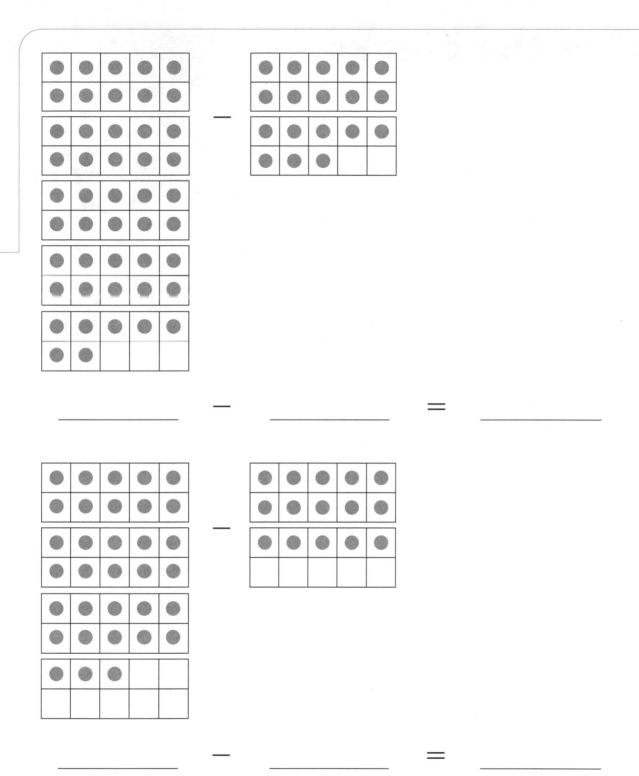

_____ − _____ = _____

_____ − _____ = _____

Fill In the Blanks

Bellwether has 12 binders in her arms. There are 5 binders on the ground. There is a difference of 7 binders.

Solve each subtraction sentence. Use the space below each subtraction sentence to show your work.

$60 - 50 =$ _____

$25 - 5 =$ _____

$14 - 12 =$ _____

$29 - 18 =$ _____

Function Box

Judy uses her quick reflexes to hand out many parking tickets.

Find the difference for each subtraction sentence.

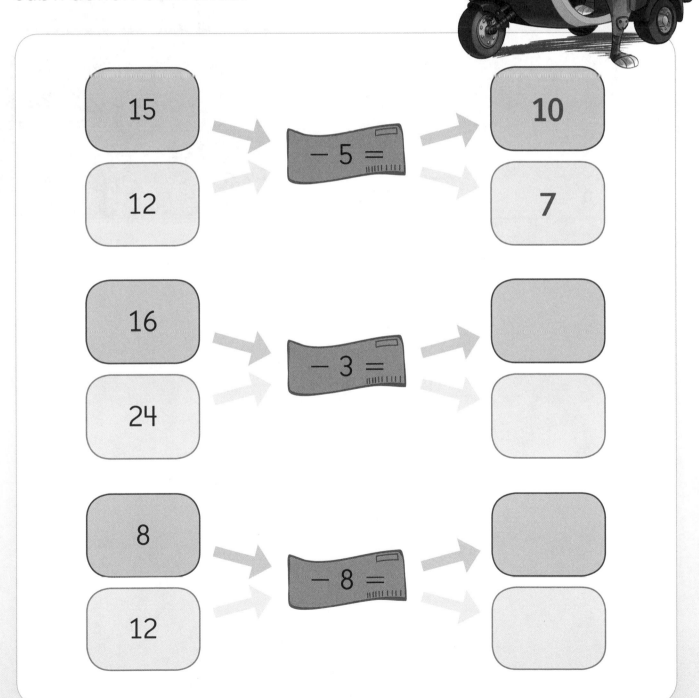

15 → − 5 = → 10

12 → − 5 = → 7

16 → − 3 =

24 → − 3 =

8 → − 8 =

12 → − 8 =

Crack the Code

What does Tamatoa love best? To find out, use mental math strategies to complete the addition sentences. Then crack the code!

2 + 9 = _____ S

9 + 4 = _____ E

9 + 8 = _____ A

8 + 7 = _____ R

5 + 9 = _____ T

9 + 7 = _____ U

Shiny

| 14 | 15 | 13 | 17 | 11 | 16 | 15 | 13 |

HINT Use mental math strategies, such as the make 10 strategy.

Matching

There are 11 Kakamora on Maui's boat. 6 Kakamora leave the boat. There is a difference of 5 Kakamora left.

11 − 6 = 5

Complete the subtraction sentences. Draw a line to the correct difference. The first one is done for you.

7 − 1 =   6

            5

5 − 2 =   4

            3

8 − 8 =   0

            8

9 − 7 =   2

            9

10 − 5 =   15

            5

15 − 10 =   20

            5

Fill In the Blanks

Little Moana reaches for a shiny stone in the ocean. The heart of Te Fiti is very special. It is not like other rocks.

Use each array to complete the addition statement and multiplication statement.

___ + ___ + ___ = ___

___ × ___ = ___

___ + ___ + ___ + ___ + ___ = ___

___ × ___ = ___

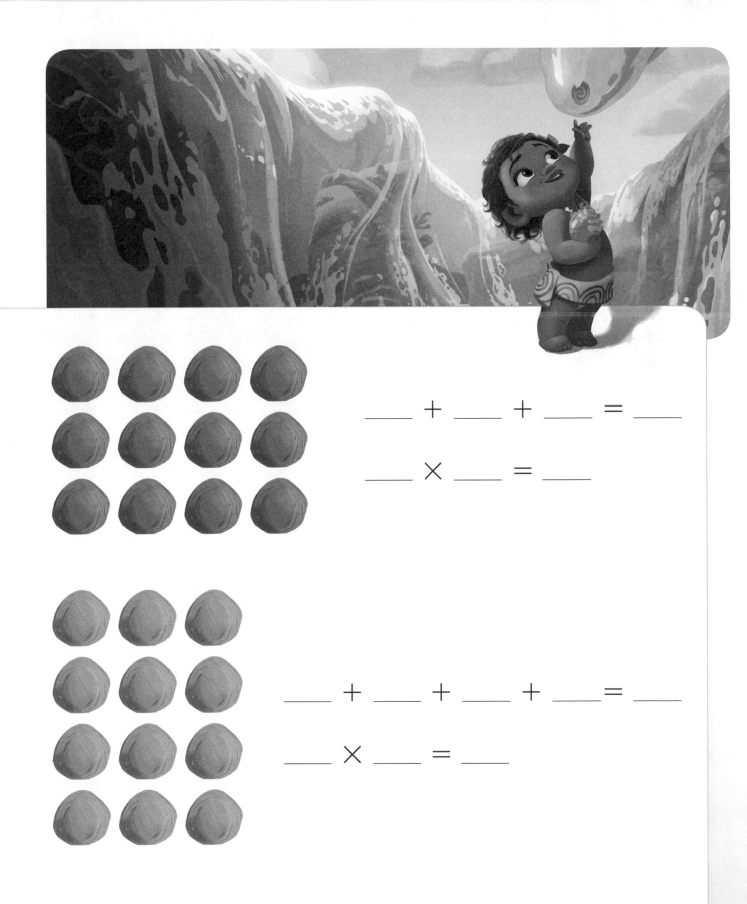

___ + ___ + ___ = ___

___ × ___ = ___

___ + ___ + ___ + ___ = ___

___ × ___ = ___

Picture Clues

The ZPD officers throw their hats in the air.

Write a multiplication sentence for each set. The first one is done for you.

Here are __2__ groups of __2__ hats.

__2__ × __2__ = __4__

There are __4__ hats altogether.

Here are ____ groups of ____ traffic cones.

____ × ____ = ____

There are ____ traffic cones altogether.

Here are ____ groups of ____ badges.

____ × ____ = ____

There are ____ badges altogether.

Here are ____ groups of ____ hats.

____ × ____ = ____

There are ____ hats altogether.

Picture Clues

The Kakamora use coconuts for armour. 12 Kakamora attack Moana. There are 3 equal groups. Each group has 4 Kakamora.

Circle groups of coconuts to show each division sentence. Complete each division sentence.

$12 \div 3 =$ ___

$6 \div 3 =$ ___

$8 \div 2 = \underline{}$

$9 \div 3 = \underline{}$

$16 \div 4 = \underline{}$

$10 \div 2 = \underline{}$

Fill In the Blanks

Moana finds treasures in a cave. The treasures have different values, just like coins.

Complete the addition sentences for the coins shown.

 +

_____ ¢ + _____ ¢ = _____ ¢

 +

_____ ¢ + _____ ¢ = _____ ¢

 + +

_____ ¢ + _____ ¢ + _____ ¢ = _____ ¢

_____ ¢ + _____ ¢ = _____ ¢

_____ ¢ + _____ ¢ + _____ ¢ = _____ ¢

_____ ¢ + _____ ¢ + _____ ¢ = _____ ¢

_____ ¢ + _____ ¢ + _____ ¢ = _____ ¢

_____ ¢ + _____ ¢ = _____ ¢

HINT You can skip count each group of coins.

47

Colour to Complete

Judy hands out tickets. When the time in a parking meter expires, the meter shows red.

Solve each subtraction sentence. Colour the parking meter. Use the Colour Key.

Colour Key
 15 cents   50 cents   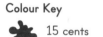 75 cents

 —

_____ ¢ — _____ ¢ = _____ ¢

    —

_____ ¢ — _____ ¢ = _____ ¢

 —

_____ ¢ — _____ ¢ = _____ ¢

 —

_____ ¢ — _____ ¢ = _____ ¢

 —

_____ ¢ — _____ ¢ = _____ ¢

 —

_____ ¢ — _____ ¢ = _____ ¢

 —

_____ ¢ — _____ ¢ = _____ ¢

Picture Clues

Sina wears a big pink flower in her hair. There are many different flowers on the island of Motunui. How can you sort them?

Sort these flowers into 2 categories.

Write a **1** under the flowers with white petals.

Write a **2** under the flowers with red petals.

———   ———   ———

———   ———

———   ———   ———

HINT One flower will not fit either of these 2 categories.

Sort these flowers into 2 categories.

Write 2 sorting rules and label the flowers.

_____

_____

_____   _____   _____

_____   _____

_____   _____   _____

HINT You can sort by colour, number of petals,
or whether the flowers have leaves.

Word Search

Ice cream cones come in 3 sizes at Jumbeaux's Café. The word **size** can be used to describe objects found in patterns.

Find words about patterns in the word search.

R E P E A T I N G   CORE

V C O R E M Z Q M   NUMBER

C O L O U R U Z U   SHAPE

A T T R I B U T E   REPEATING

I S E F D C Z H R   COLOUR

N U M B E R A L C   SIZE

M C Q L S H A P E   LETTER

U L E T T E R K D   ATTRIBUTE

W L B S I Z E H S

H C O Q D Z T E V

Fill In the Blanks

Jumbo-pops come in different colours.

What changes in each of the patterns below? Write what changes beside each pattern.

Word Bank

colour   shape   size

_____

_____

_____

_____

HINT There might be more than one attribute changing in a pattern.

Matching

Moana sees patterns in the tapa images of her ancestors.

To extend each pattern, draw a line to the correct set of images.

HINT Look at each image in the pattern carefully.

Colour to Complete

The triangles around Maui's neck show a repeating pattern.

<u>Underline</u> the core of each pattern. Then extend the pattern by adding the next 3 shapes.

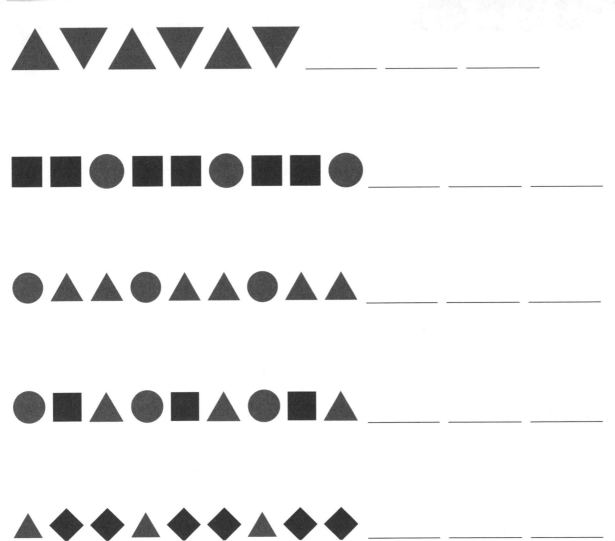

Crack the Code

Judy looks for patterns to help her solve crimes.

Who helps her? To find out, extend each pattern. Then crack the code!

————————
1

————————
2

————————
3

————————
4

Letter Code

A ⬤   K ▲   D ⬤   I ▲

N ■   C ▲   S ■

___ ___ ___ ___
1   2   3   4

HINT Match each shape and number to a letter to crack the code.

Colour to Complete

Nick needs a red Jumbo-pop.

Colour the Jumbo-pops to create patterns.

Create an AB pattern.

Create an ABB pattern.

Create an AAB pattern.

Create an ABC pattern.

Fill In the Blanks

Moana leaves the secret cave feeling excited. Her ancestors sailed the open sea!

(Circle) each pattern core. Use words to describe the pattern core.

_____

_____

_____

59

Fill In the Blanks

Emmitt Otterton is missing. But Judy is on the case! She wants to find all 14 missing mammals.

Determine the missing number in each equation. Use the space below each equation to show your work.

$11 + 4 =$ _____ $+ 7$

$10 - 6 = 8 -$ _____

$3 +$ _____ $= 1 + 5$

_____ $+ 7 = 3 + 4$

HINT Use manipulatives, such as counters or blocks, to model each side of the equation.

Fill In the Blanks

Chief Bogo is not impressed by the bag of stolen onions on his desk.

There are 11 onions. The mouldy onions are removed. 6 onions are left. How many moldy onions are there?

To solve this problem, write it out like this: $11 - \underline{\quad} = 6$.

Determine each missing number. Use the blank space below each equation to show your work.

$3 + \underline{\quad} = 8$

$14 - \underline{\quad} = 7$

$12 - \underline{\quad} = 4$

$\underline{\quad} + 8 = 18$

$8 - \underline{\quad} = 2$

$\underline{\quad} + 9 = 10$

Maze

Help Moana and Maui get away from Tamatoa. Follow the greater numbers.

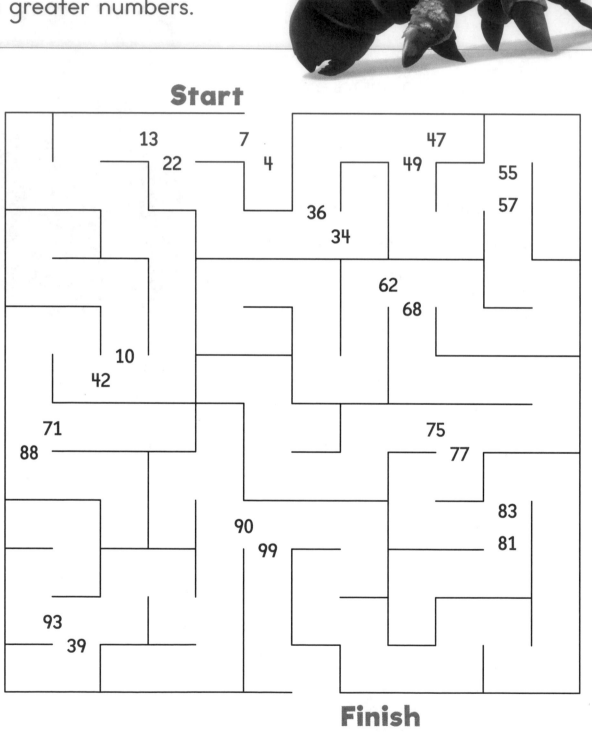

Start

13
22
7
4
47
49
55
57
36
34
62
68
10
42
71
88
75
77
83
81
90
99
93
39

Finish

Now, help Moana and Maui continue their journey. Follow the lesser numbers.

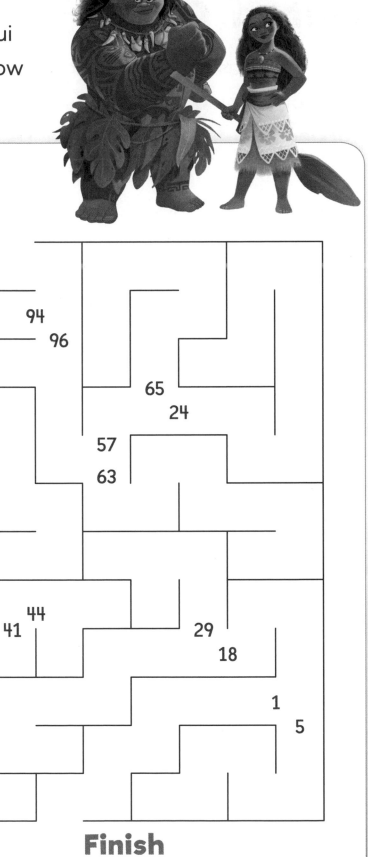

Start

94
89
96
88
74
72
65
24
57
63
58
65
53
67
44
41
29
18
39 33
1
5
11 92

Finish

Out of Order

Judy's job as a meter maid is all about timing. She hands out parking tickets when time expires on the meter.

Number these parking tickets in order from earliest to latest.
Write **1** beside the earliest ticket.
Write **6** beside the latest ticket.

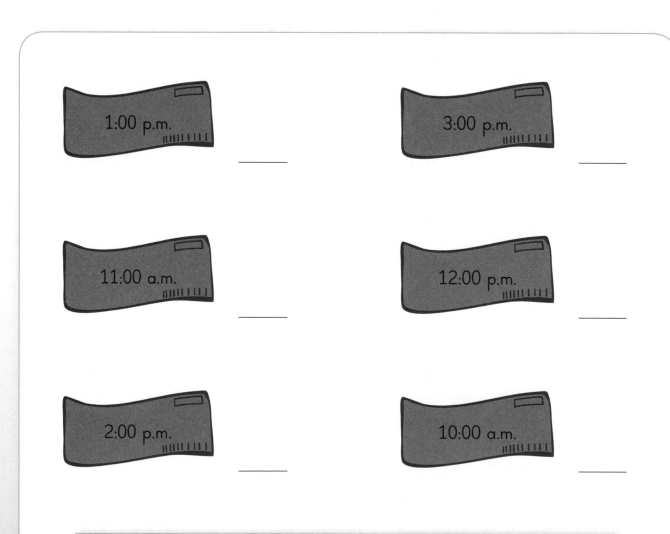

1:00 p.m. _____

3:00 p.m. _____

11:00 a.m. _____

12:00 p.m. _____

2:00 p.m. _____

10:00 a.m. _____

HINT Remember that p.m. occurs later than a.m. in a day.

Matching

Nick puts a lot of time into his hustles. His schedule is very organized.

Match each timed activity with the correct clock.

Meet Finnick at 10:30 a.m.

Go to Jumbeaux's Café at 10:45 a.m.

Melt the Jumbo-pop at 11:00 a.m.

Sell pawpsicles at 11:45 a.m.

Count the profits at 1:15 p.m.

Matching

Judy packs her favourite things into her suitcase when she moves to Zootopia. The length of a suitcase can be measured in centimetres.

Match each item to the most appropriate unit of measurement that should be used to determine length.

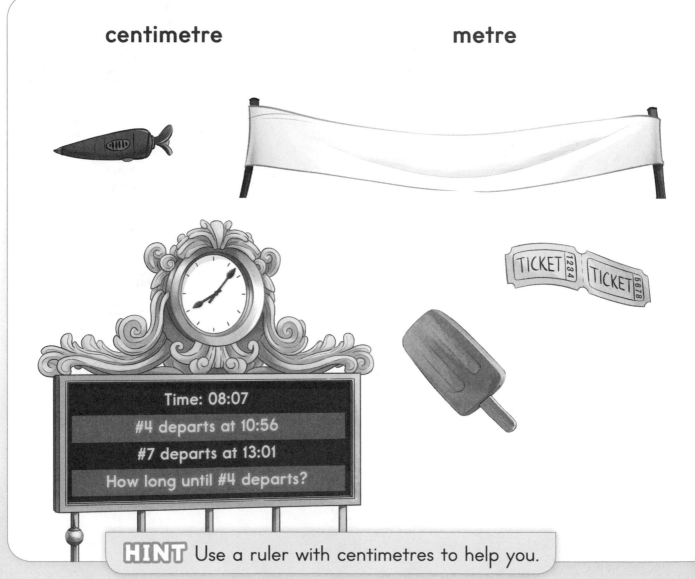

centimetre   **metre**

Time: 08:07

#4 departs at 10:56

#7 departs at 13:01

How long until #4 departs?

HINT Use a ruler with centimetres to help you.

Match each item to the most appropriate
unit of measurement that should be used
to determine mass.

grams   kilograms

HINT A gram is about the mass of a paper clip.

Fill In the Blanks

Moana uses her hand to measure the stars. You can also use your finger to measure things. Look at the width of your pointer finger.

Estimate: This turtle is about _____ finger widths long.

The length of this turtle is _____ finger widths long.

Estimate: This fish is about _____ finger widths long.

The length of this fish is _____ finger widths long.

68

Out of Order

The villagers of Motunui play many different drums.

Look at the width of your pointer finger. Measure the height of each drum. Then order these drums by height from shortest to tallest.

_____

_____   _____   _____
finger widths   finger widths   finger widths

HINT Write **1** beside the shortest drum.
Write **3** beside the tallest drum.

Fill In the Blanks

Mr. and Mrs. Hopps are farmers.
They plant carrots, potatoes,
and kale in their garden.

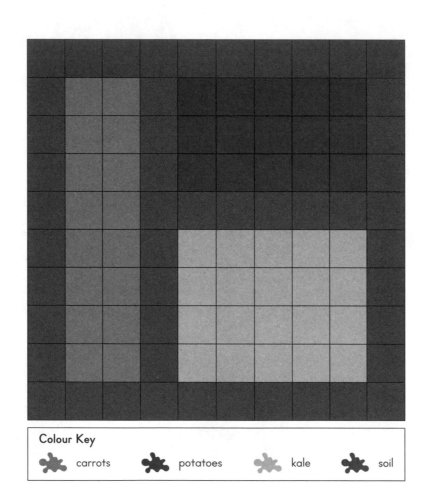

Colour Key

carrots   potatoes   kale   soil

How much of the garden is used to grow carrots?

_____ squares

How much of the garden is used to grow potatoes?

_____ squares

How much of the garden is used to grow kale?

_____ squares

Which vegetable takes up the greatest space
in the garden?

_____

Which vegetable takes up the least space?

_____

How much of the garden is soil?

_____ squares

HINT Area is the number of square
units needed to cover a shape.

Colour to Complete

Help the Hopps plan their garden for next year.

Colour the grid to show how you would plant the vegetables. Use the Colour Key. Each square represents one plant.

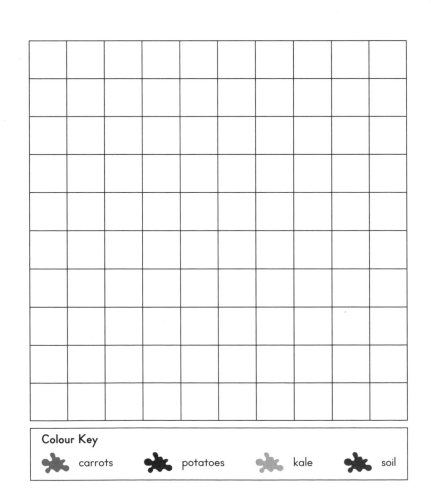

Colour Key

carrots   potatoes   kale   soil

How much of the garden is used to grow carrots?

_____ squares

How much of the garden is used to grow potatoes?

_____ squares

How much of the garden is used to grow kale?

_____ squares

Which vegetable takes up the greatest space
in the garden?

_____

Which vegetable takes up the least space?

_____

How much of the garden is soil?

_____ squares

Out of Order

Zootopia police officers are all very different.

Order the characters by mass from lightest to heaviest. Write **1** below the lightest character and **4** below the heaviest

———————   ———————   ———————   ———————

Out of Order

Nick and Finnick fill empty water bottles with rainwater. They take the water bottles to Sahara Square and sell them.

Order the containers by capacity from least to greatest.

_____   _____   _____   _____

Fill In the Blanks

Moana washes up on shore after a storm. How do you prepare for stormy weather?

Use the words in the Word Bank to complete each sentence.

1. It is warm outside and you have decided to go swimming. Time to change into a _____.

2. A cold wind starts and your ears get cold. You should put on a

   _____.

3. It gets a bit cooler. Your T-shirt is not warm enough. Time to put on a _____.

4. The weather is getting colder. The rain turns to ice rain, and then it turns to

   _____.

Word Bank

snow   hat

jacket

swimsuit

Are these temperatures rising or falling?
(Circle) **rising** or **falling** in the space provided.

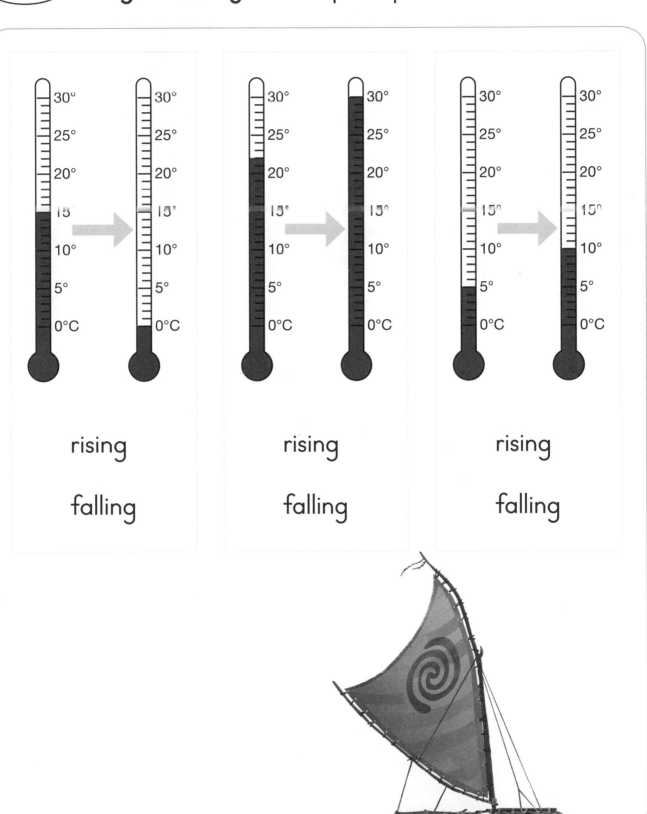

rising

falling

rising

falling

rising

falling

Matching

Judy has a busy day ahead of her! Determine the best time for Judy to do these activities.

Draw a line to match each activity to a time of day.

| Get dressed for work. | Have dinner. | Take a walk in the park. |

Beginning of the day   **Middle of the day**   **End of the day**

| Have lunch. | Take a shower. | Call Mom and Dad. |

HINT You might have more than one line going to a part of the day.

Fill In the Blanks

Judy loves her job! She uses a clock to get to work on time.

Show what time you wake up for school.

Show what time you eat lunch.

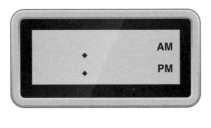

Show what time you go to bed.

Matching

Judy's badge is a unique shape. Match each shape to its description.

 3 edges and 3 vertices

 no edges or vertices

 6 edges and 6 vertices

 4 equal edges and 4 vertices

 5 edges and 5 vertices

 2 long edges and 2 short edges, and 4 vertices

 8 edges and 8 vertices

 8 edges and 8 vertices

HINT Another word for **vertices** is **corners**.

Picture Clues

Nick is looking out the window of the subway car. That window is shaped like a rectangle.

What other shapes do you see in this scene? Label some of the shapes you see.

Colour to Complete

Gramma Tala tells the tale of Te Fiti to a group of village children. She is holding up 2 pictures that have 4 sides.

How many sides does each of these shapes have? Colour the shapes. Use the Colour Key.

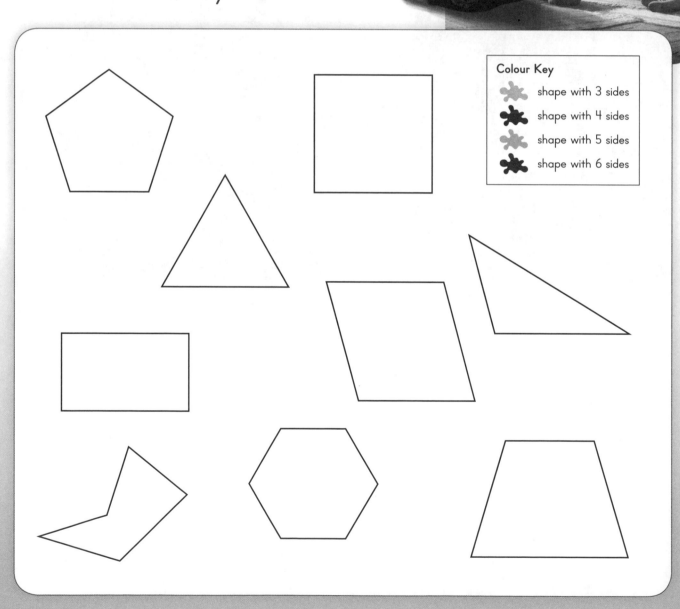

Colour Key

shape with 3 sides

shape with 4 sides

shape with 5 sides

shape with 6 sides

Matching

Moana finds boats in a cave. The sails on the boats have 3 sides.

Look at the shapes in each circle. Determine the sorting rule.

Sorting rule. _____

_____

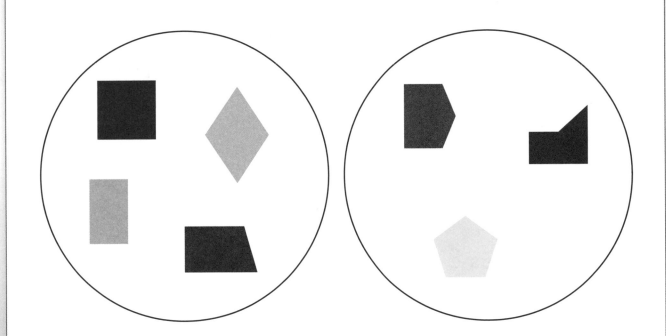

Where do these shapes belong? Draw a line from each shape to the correct circle.

Fill In the Blanks

Judy wants to solve the missing mammal case.

Identify each shape. Use the shapes listed in the Word Bank.

Chief Bogo's clipboard has 4 sides. 2 sides are short. 2 sides are long. What shape is the clipboard?

_____

The back of Judy's chair has 4 equal sides. What shape is it?

_____

A stop sign has 8 sides. What shape is it?

_____

In baseball, the home plate has 5 sides.

What shape is it? _____

Word Bank

square

rectangle

octagon

pentagon

HINT Use words from the Word Bank.

Colour to Complete

Judy's shirt and Nick's tie have geometric patterns.

Colour the shapes to create a geometric design. Use the Colour Key.

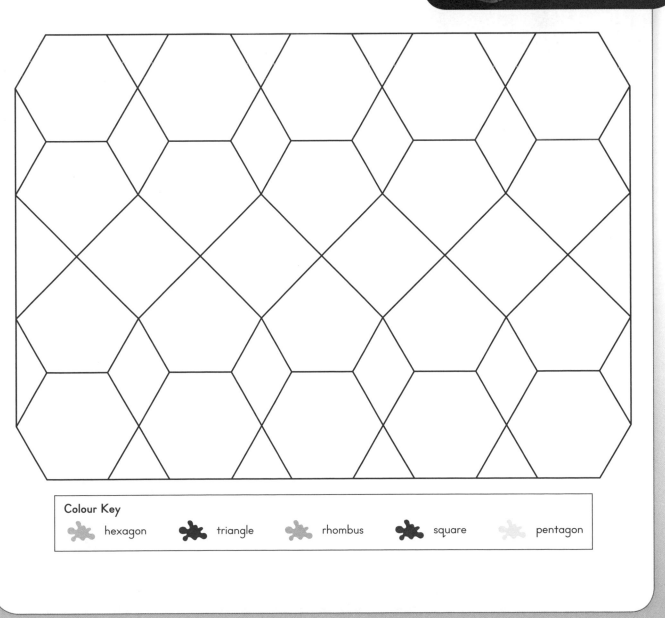

Colour Key

hexagon   triangle   rhombus   square   pentagon

Matching

Pua is standing on a rock.
The rock is symmetrical.

Make symmetrical shapes by
matching the halves.

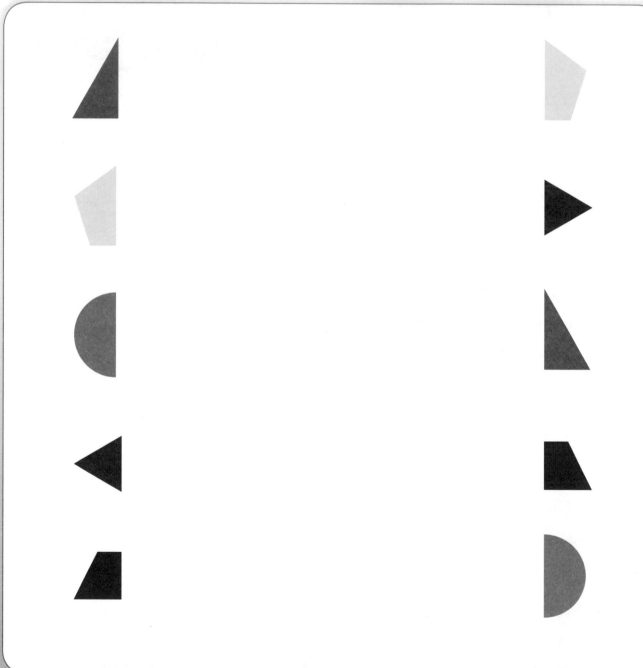

Picture Clues

There are a lot of shells
on the island of Motunui.
Some shells are symmetrical.

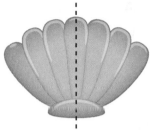

Draw all the lines of symmetry on
each shape. How many lines of
symmetry does each shape have?

_____ line(s)
of symmetry

_____ line(s)
of symmetry

_____ line(s)
of symmetry

_____ line(s)
of symmetry

_____ line(s)
of symmetry

_____ line(s)
of symmetry

HINT Trace each shape on paper. Cut out the shape. Fold the
shape in half in different ways. Determine the line(s) of symmetry.

Word Search

Duke Weaselton holds a bag shaped like a rectangular prism.

Find prism words in the word search.

VERTICES   SIDE   VERTEX

EDGE   FACE

O Z Z V F P A K

R Z G X Z D S Y

L T W O Z Y V Q

P V E R T E X P

F A W S I D E L

K H W Q F A C E

V E R T I C E S

P E D G E K A R

HINT As you look for a word, think about what it means.

Matching

Judy talks to her parents after a long day. The phone she is holding is shaped like a rectangular prism.

Match each 3-D object to the correct name.

cone

sphere

pyramid

cube

cylinder

Picture Search

With your finger, trace the yellow path that Heihei can follow to reach Pua.

Word Bank

around   above   below   over   through

under   to the right   to the left   on

Describe the path Heihei takes.

_____

_____

_____

_____

Describe the path Pua might take to get to Heihei.

_____

_____

_____

_____

HINT Use the words in the Word Bank to describe each path.

91

Picture Clues

Officer Clawhauser keeps a jar of candy on his desk.
Imagine that the candies below are the only ones left
in the jar.

(Circle) the word that best describes each sentence.

Officer Clawhauser will draw a candy
from the jar.

likely   unlikely   certain   impossible

Officer Clawhauser will draw a blue candy
from the jar.

likely   unlikely   certain   impossible

Officer Clawhauser will draw a yellow
candy from the jar.

likely   unlikely   certain   impossible

Officer Clawhauser will draw an orange
candy from the jar.

likely   unlikely   certain   impossible

Write your own probability sentences about these candies.

It is likely that _____

_____

It is impossible for _____

_____

It is certain that _____

_____

Picture Clues

Little Moana is collecting coconuts.
She sees Heihei trip over a rock.

How many rocks and coconuts
are there? Take a tally
to record the data.

Tally of rocks:

There are _____ rocks.

Tally of coconuts:

There are _____ coconuts.

HINT When you tally, 1 is shown like this: | .
5 is shown like this: ||||| .

94

Graphing

Little Moana and her friends draw pictures of things on the island.

This tally chart shows the number of pictures they draw of each item.

Pictures	Tally
Coconuts	|||
Shells	|||||	
Boats	||||

Add a title and labels to complete the pictograph.

_____

_____

_____ ◯ ◯ ◯ ◯

_____ ◯ ◯ ◯ ◯ ◯ ◯

_____ ◯ ◯ ◯ ◯

One ◯ represents 1 picture drawn.

Graphing

Customers at Jumbeaux's Café try different ice cream flavours.

In one hour, Jumbeaux sells 6 chocolate cones, 5 vanilla cones, 8 strawberry cones, and 4 orange cones.

Use tally marks to represent all the cones sold.

Flavour	Tally
Chocolate	
Vanilla	
Strawberry	
Orange	

Which flavour is the most popular?

_____

Which flavour is the least popular?

_____

Use the information in the tally chart to complete the pictograph. Draw one brown triangle for each cone Jumbeaux's Café sells.

Popular Flavours at Jumbeaux's Café

Chocolate

Vanilla

Strawberry

Orange

One ▼ represents 1 cone.

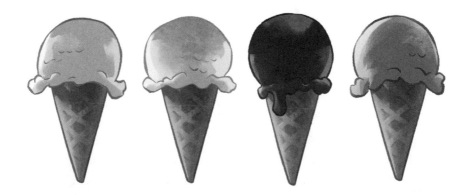

Graphing

Moana and Gramma Tala collect shells. How many shells of each colour are there?

Create a tally chart for the shells.

Colour of Shell	Tally
Blue	
Green	
Purple	

Use the tally chart to create a bar graph.
Remember to include a title and labels.

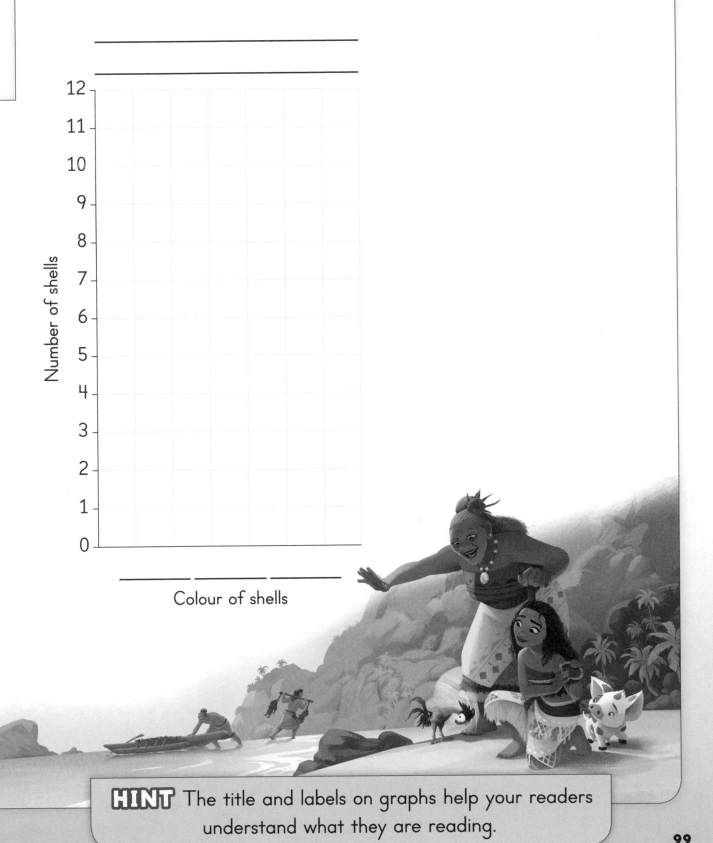

Number of shells

12
11
10
9
8
7
6
5
4
3
2
1
0

Colour of shells

HINT The title and labels on graphs help your readers
understand what they are reading.

Answers

Fill In the Blanks

Officer Clawhauser greets hundreds of visitors every day.

Fill in the missing numbers in the 100-chart.

1	2	3	4	5	6	7	8	9	10
11	12	13	14	15	16	17	18	19	20
21	22	23	24	25	26	27	28	29	30
31	32	33	34	35	36	37	38	39	40
41	42	43	44	45	46	47	48	49	50
51	52	53	54	55	56	57	58	59	60
61	62	63	64	65	66	67	68	69	70
71	72	73	74	75	76	77	78	79	80
81	82	83	84	85	86	87	88	89	90
91	92	93	94	95	96	97	98	99	100

4

Crack the Code

What is Judy's motto about Zootopia?

To find out, skip count by 5s. Then crack the code!

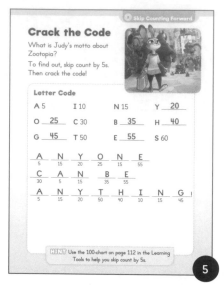

Letter Code

A 5	I 10	N 15	Y _20_
O _25_	C 30	B _35_	H _40_
G _45_	T 50	E _55_	S 60

A N Y O N E
5 15 20 25 15 55

C A N B E
30 5 15 35 55

A N Y T H I N G
5 15 20 50 40 10 15 45

HINT Use the 100-chart on page 112 in the Learning Tools to help you skip count by 5s.

5

Connect the Dots

Moana walks into a secret cave. What does she see? Start at 30. Count backward by 1s. Connect the dots.

6

Maze

Moana reads the stars to return the heart to Te Fiti.

Skip count backward by 10s to complete the maze.

7

Colour to Complete

Sina and Tui are collecting coconuts.

Show 34 coconuts using these 10-frames.

Show 67 coconuts using these 10-frames.

8

9

Matching

Thirty-two Kakamora are attacking Moana. Thirty-two can also be shown using the number 32.

Draw a line to match the word to the number.

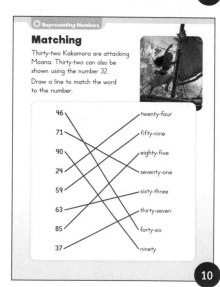

46 — forty-six
71 — seventy-one
90 — ninety
24 — twenty-four
59 — fifty-nine
63 — sixty-three
85 — eighty-five
37 — thirty-seven

10

Picture

Moana returns to Motunui. Base ten blocks can be used to represent the population of villages like Motunui. Sketch each number using base ten blocks.

22

41

68

99

HINT You can sketch a tens rod like this. You can sketch a ones block like this.

11

Fill In the Blanks

Judy takes the train to Zootopia. The train cars are in order by number.

Label the train cars with numbers from the Number Bank. Order these numbers from greatest to least. The first one is done for you.

Number Bank

39   56   93   16   65   88

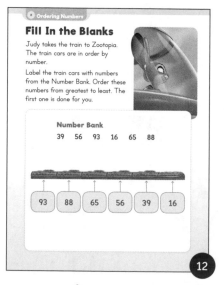

| 93 | 88 | 65 | 56 | 39 | 16 |

12

*Sample answers provided.

Fill In the Blanks

Judy Hopps answers questions from reporters.

Label the badges with numbers from the Number Bank. Order these numbers from least to greatest. The first one is done for you.

Number Bank

| 54 | 21 | 99 |
| 12 | 33 | 76 |

99
76
54
33
21
12

Colour to Complete

Nick has a cooler full of pawpsicles. He sells them to the lemmings. Colour the pawpsicle in each set that shows the lesser number.

19	**17**		**32**	36
21	**20**		**28**	32
89	**78**		**60**	65
100	**99**		55	**53**

Circling

Judy trains hard. She does each exercise many times. Circle the greater number in each set.

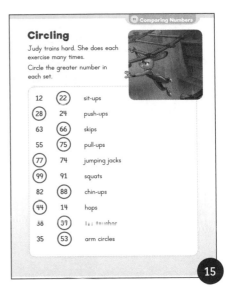

12	(22)	sit-ups
(28)	24	push-ups
63	(66)	skips
55	(75)	pull-ups
(77)	74	jumping jacks
(99)	91	squats
82	(88)	chin-ups
(44)	14	hops
38	(39)	leg raises
35	(53)	arm circles

Picture Clues

Little Moana likes to collect shells. She has 5 shells.

Look at each set of shells. Estimate. Then count.

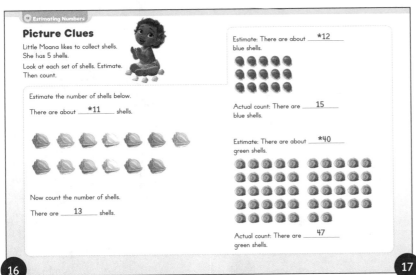

Estimate the number of shells below.

There are about ___*11___ shells.

Now count the number of shells.

There are ___13___ shells.

Estimate: There are about ___*12___ blue shells.

Actual count: There are ___15___ blue shells.

Estimate: There are about ___*40___ green shells.

Actual count: There are ___47___ green shells.

Word Search

The lemmings love pawpsicles. They pay Nick. Nick needs to make change.

Identify each coin. Circle its name in the word search.

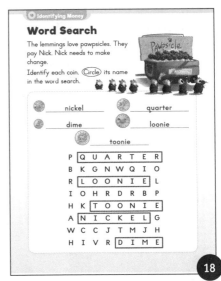

___nickel___   ___quarter___

___dime___   ___loonie___

___toonie___

P	Q U A R T E R
B	K G N W Q I O
R	L O O N I E L
I	O H R D R B P
H	K T O O N I E
A	N I C K E L G
W	C C J T M J H
H	I V R D I M E

Matching

Nick and Finnick love to make money. Match each group of coins to how much it is worth.

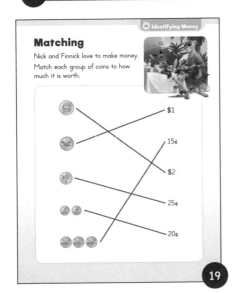

$1
15¢
$2
25¢
20¢

Fill In the Blanks

All this treasure must be valuable! Estimate the value of each set of coins. Then count to find the actual value.

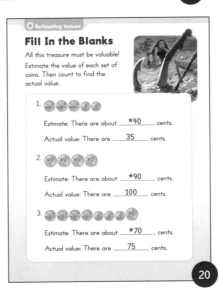

1. Estimate: There are about ___*40___ cents.
   Actual value: There are ___35___ cents.

2. Estimate: There are about ___*90___ cents.
   Actual value: There are ___100___ cents.

3. Estimate: There are about ___*70___ cents.
   Actual value: There are ___75___ cents.

Picture Clues

Maui's fishhook is more valuable than all the treasure. Circle the coins in each pair that have a greater value.

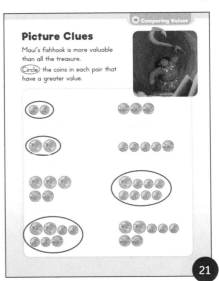

---

*Sample answers provided.

Answers

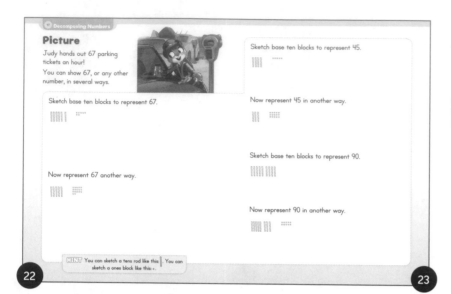

Picture

Judy hands out 67 parking tickets an hour!

You can show 67, or any other number, in several ways.

Sketch base ten blocks to represent 67.

Now represent 67 another way.

Sketch base ten blocks to represent 45.

Now represent 45 in another way.

Sketch base ten blocks to represent 90.

Now represent 90 in another way.

HINT You can sketch a tens rod like this: | . You can sketch a ones block like this: ·.

23

Matching

Gideon Grey bakes pies. How much pie is left? Match each pie to the correct fraction words.

one fourth

one half

one third

How much of each shape is coloured in? Match each picture to the correct fraction words.

one fourth

one third

three fourths

two thirds

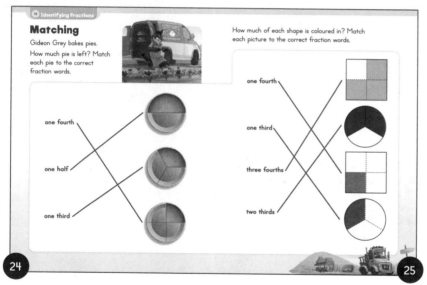

Colour to Complete

When Te Fiti smiles, life blooms again on the island of Motunui.

Colour one fourth of this flower.

Colour one third of this flower.

Colour one half of this flower.

Colour one third of this flower.

Colour one fourth of the flowers.

Colour one third of the flowers.

Colour one half of the flowers.

Colour one third of the flowers.

HINT Where there are 4 equal parts, we call each part a fourth or a quarter. Two quarters equals one half.

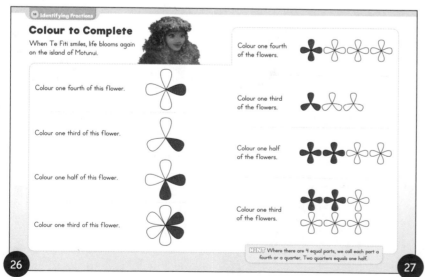

Crossword

Maui holds one fish. You could use **one** or **1** to represent that number.

Complete the crossword. Write the number word for each number. The first one is done for you.

Across
1. 19
3. 17
5. 14
8. 10
10. 13
11. 16

Down
2. 12
4. 11
6. 20
7. 15
9. 18

HINT If you do not have as many letters as squares, check the spelling of your number word.

*Sample answers provided.

Function Box

Moana is playing with 1 shell. If she adds 0 shells, she still has 1 shell to play with.

Determine the sum. Then determine the difference.

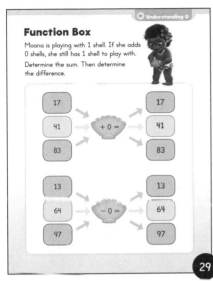

17		17
41	+ 0 =	41
83		83

13		13
64	– 0 =	64
97		97

Fill In the Blanks

Chief Tui tells Moana about the pile of stones each chief has added to.

Solve the addition sentences. Then write the number word. The first one is done for you.

10 + 10 20	15 + 15 30	40 + 40 80
twenty	thirty	eighty
20 + 20 40	35 + 35 70	25 + 25 50
forty	seventy	fifty
30 + 30 60	5 + 5 10	45 + 45 90
sixty	ten	ninety

Picture Clues

Maui is a master fisher. The fish seem to be drawn to his boat.

Count the fish in each set. Write an addition sentence and solve.

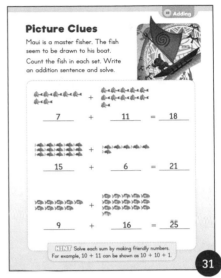

__7__ + __11__ = __18__

__15__ + __6__ = __21__

__9__ + __16__ = __25__

HINT Solve each sum by making friendly numbers. For example, 10 + 11 can be shown as 10 + 10 + 1.

Colour to Complete

Officer Clawhauser loves doughnuts. Colour the doughnuts. Use the Colour Key.

Colour Key
55
81
35
24
47
39

22 + 2 = __24__   30 + 17 = __47__

20 + 15 = __35__   29 + 10 = __39__

25 + 30 = __55__   40 + 41 = __81__

HINT Use mental math strategies to help you find the sum.

Solve the Riddle

Judy looks for clues to solve a crime. What has four legs but does not walk? Calculate each sum. Then solve the riddle.

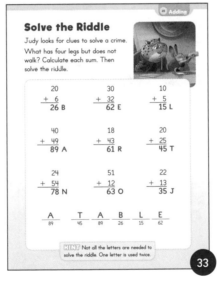

20 + 6 26 B	30 + 32 62 E	10 + 5 15 L
40 + 49 89 A	18 + 43 61 R	20 + 25 45 T
24 + 54 78 N	51 + 12 63 O	22 + 13 35 J

<u>A</u> <u>T</u> <u>A</u> <u>B</u> <u>L</u> <u>E</u>
89   45   89   26   15   62

HINT Not all the letters are needed to solve the riddle. One letter is used twice.

Fill In the Blanks

Moana uses resources from the land to repair her boat. You can use resources, such as counters, to help you subtract. Write each subtraction sentence.

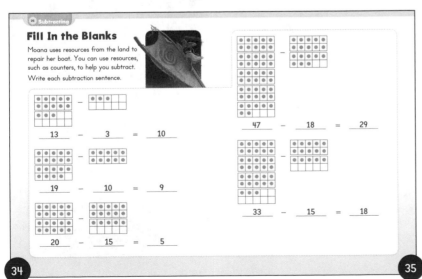

__13__ – __3__ = __10__

__19__ – __10__ = __9__

__20__ – __15__ = __5__

__47__ – __18__ = __29__

__33__ – __15__ = __18__

Fill In the Blanks

Bellwether has 12 binders in her arms. There are 5 binders on the ground. There is a difference of 7 binders. Solve each subtraction sentence. Use the space below each subtraction sentence to show your work.

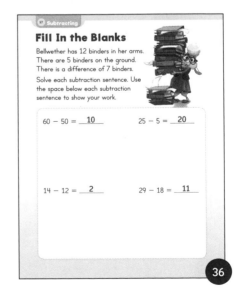

60 – 50 = __10__   25 – 5 = __20__

14 – 12 = __2__   29 – 18 = __11__

---

*Sample answers provided.

Answers

Function Box

Judy uses her quick reflexes to hand out many parking tickets.

Find the difference for each subtraction sentence.

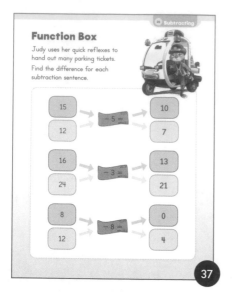

15 → $-5=$ → 10

12 → → 7

16 → $-3=$ → 13

24 → → 21

8 → $-8=$ → 0

12 → → 4

37

Crack the Code

What does Tamatoa love best? To find out, use mental math strategies to complete the addition sentences. Then crack the code!

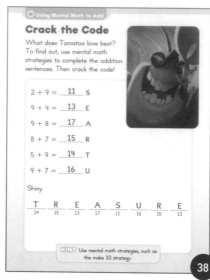

$2 + 9 = \underline{11}$ S

$9 + 4 = \underline{13}$ E

$9 + 8 = \underline{17}$ A

$8 + 7 = \underline{15}$ R

$5 + 9 = \underline{14}$ T

$9 + 7 = \underline{16}$ U

Shiny

T	R	E	A	S	U	R	E
14	15	13	17	11	16	15	13

HINT Use mental math strategies, such as the make 10 strategy.

38

Matching

There are 11 Kakamora on Maui's boat. 6 Kakamora leave the boat. There is a difference of 5 Kakamora left.

$11 - 6 = 5$

Complete the subtraction sentences. Draw a line to the correct difference. The first one is done for you.

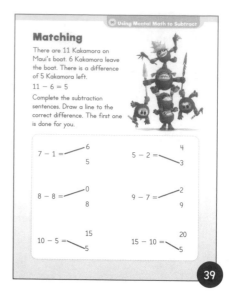

$7 - 1 =$ → 6
5

$5 - 2 =$ 4
→ 3

$8 - 8 =$ → 0
8

$9 - 7 =$ → 2
9

$10 - 5 =$ 15
→ 5

$15 - 10 =$ 20
→ 5

39

Fill In the Blanks

Little Moana reaches for a shiny stone in the ocean. The heart of Te Fiti is very special. It is not like other rocks.

Use each array to complete the addition statement and multiplication statement.

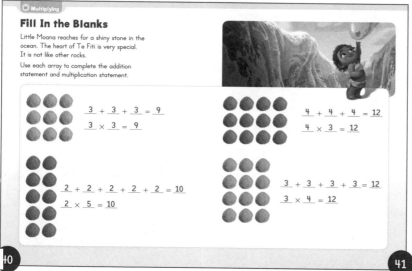

$\underline{3} + \underline{3} + \underline{3} = \underline{9}$
$\underline{3} \times \underline{3} = \underline{9}$

$\underline{4} + \underline{4} + \underline{4} = \underline{12}$
$\underline{4} \times \underline{3} = \underline{12}$

$\underline{2} + \underline{2} + \underline{2} + \underline{2} + \underline{2} = \underline{10}$
$\underline{2} \times \underline{5} = \underline{10}$

$\underline{3} + \underline{3} + \underline{3} + \underline{3} = \underline{12}$
$\underline{3} \times \underline{4} = \underline{12}$

40

41

Picture Clues

The ZPD officers throw their hats in the air. Write a multiplication sentence for each set. The first one is done for you.

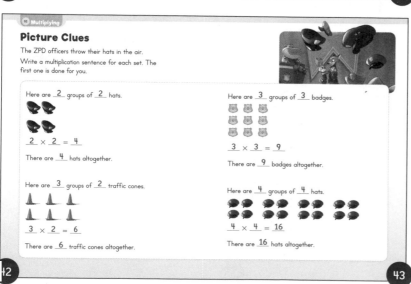

Here are $\underline{2}$ groups of $\underline{2}$ hats.

$\underline{2} \times \underline{2} = \underline{4}$

There are $\underline{4}$ hats altogether.

Here are $\underline{3}$ groups of $\underline{2}$ traffic cones.

$\underline{3} \times \underline{2} = \underline{6}$

There are $\underline{6}$ traffic cones altogether.

Here are $\underline{3}$ groups of $\underline{3}$ badges.

$\underline{3} \times \underline{3} = \underline{9}$

There are $\underline{9}$ badges altogether.

Here are $\underline{4}$ groups of $\underline{4}$ hats.

$\underline{4} \times \underline{4} = \underline{16}$

There are $\underline{16}$ hats altogether.

42

43

*Sample answers provided.

Picture Clues

The Kakamora use coconuts for armour. 12 Kakamora attack Moana. There are 3 equal groups. Each group has 4 Kakamora.

Circle groups of coconuts to show each division sentence. Complete each division sentence.

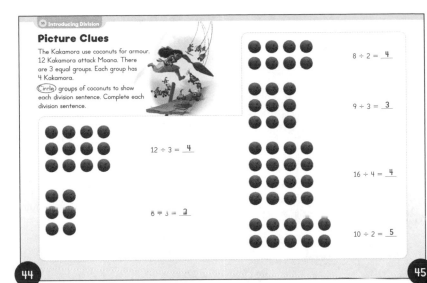

$12 \div 3 = \underline{4}$

$8 \div 3 = \underline{2}$

$8 \div 2 = \underline{4}$

$9 \div 3 = \underline{3}$

$16 \div 4 = \underline{4}$

$10 \div 2 = \underline{5}$

44 45

Fill In the Blanks

Moana finds treasures in a cave. The treasures have different values, just like coins.

Complete the addition sentences for the coins shown.

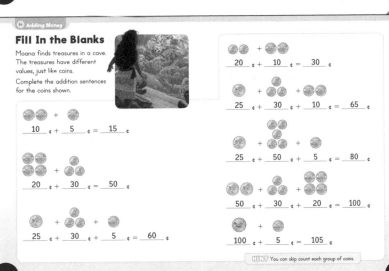

$\underline{10}$ ¢ + $\underline{5}$ ¢ = $\underline{15}$ ¢

$\underline{20}$ ¢ + $\underline{30}$ ¢ = $\underline{50}$ ¢

$\underline{25}$ ¢ + $\underline{30}$ ¢ + $\underline{5}$ ¢ = $\underline{60}$ ¢

$\underline{20}$ ¢ + $\underline{10}$ ¢ = $\underline{30}$ ¢

$\underline{25}$ ¢ + $\underline{30}$ ¢ + $\underline{10}$ ¢ = $\underline{65}$ ¢

$\underline{25}$ ¢ + $\underline{50}$ ¢ + $\underline{5}$ ¢ = $\underline{80}$ ¢

$\underline{50}$ ¢ + $\underline{30}$ ¢ + $\underline{20}$ ¢ = $\underline{100}$ ¢

$\underline{100}$ ¢ + $\underline{5}$ ¢ = $\underline{105}$ ¢

HINT You can skip count each group of coins.

46 47

Colour to Complete

Judy hands out tickets. When the time in a parking meter expires, the meter shows red.

Solve each subtraction sentence. Colour the parking meter. Use the Colour Key.

Colour Key
15 cents 50 cents 75 cents

$\underline{75}$ ¢ − $\underline{25}$ ¢ = $\underline{50}$ ¢

$\underline{30}$ ¢ − $\underline{15}$ ¢ = $\underline{15}$ ¢

$\underline{80}$ ¢ − $\underline{5}$ ¢ = $\underline{75}$ ¢

$\underline{75}$ ¢ − $\underline{60}$ ¢ = $\underline{15}$ ¢

$\underline{80}$ ¢ − $\underline{60}$ ¢ = $\underline{20}$ ¢

$\underline{75}$ ¢ − $\underline{15}$ ¢ = $\underline{60}$ ¢

$\underline{100}$ ¢ − $\underline{25}$ ¢ = $\underline{75}$ ¢

48 49

*Sample answers provided.

Answers

Picture Clues
(Sorting — page 50-51)

Sina wears a big pink flower in her hair. There are many different flowers on the island of Motunui. How can you sort them? Sort these flowers into 2 categories.

Write a 1 under the flowers with white petals.
Write a 2 under the flowers with red petals.

Sort these flowers into 2 categories.

Write 2 sorting rules and label the flowers.

*Write 1 under flowers with 3 green leaves.
*Write 2 under flowers with 0 green leaves.

HINT One flower will not fit either of these 2 categories.

HINT You can sort by colour, number of petals, or whether the flowers have leaves.

50   51

Word Search
(Identifying Patterns — page 52)

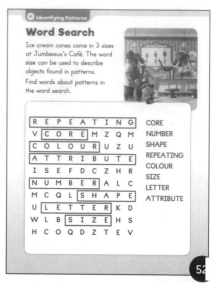

Ice cream cones come in 3 sizes at Jumbeaux's Café. The word size can be used to describe objects found in patterns.

Find words about patterns in the word search.

R	E	P	E	A	T	I	N	G
V	C	O	R	E	M	Z	Q	M
C	O	L	O	U	R	U	Z	U
A	T	T	R	I	B	U	T	E
I	S	E	F	D	C	Z	H	R
N	U	M	B	E	R	A	L	C
M	C	Q	L	S	H	A	P	E
U	L	E	T	T	E	R	K	D
W	L	B	S	I	Z	E	H	S
H	C	O	Q	D	Z	T	E	V

CORE
NUMBER
SHAPE
REPEATING
COLOUR
SIZE
LETTER
ATTRIBUTE

52

Fill In the Blanks
(Identifying Patterns — page 53)

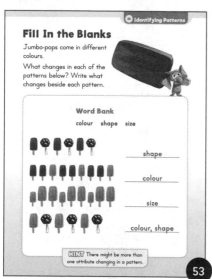

Jumbo-pops come in different colours.

What changes in each of the patterns below? Write what changes beside each pattern.

Word Bank

colour   shape   size

shape

colour

size

colour, shape

HINT There might be more than one attribute changing in a pattern.

53

Matching
(Extending Patterns — page 54)

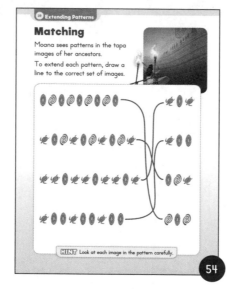

Moana sees patterns in the tapa images of her ancestors.

To extend each pattern, draw a line to the correct set of images.

HINT Look at each image in the pattern carefully.

54

Colour to Complete
(Extending Patterns — page 55)

The triangles around Maui's neck show a repeating pattern.

Underline the core of each pattern. Then extend the pattern by adding the next 3 shapes.

55

Crack the Code
(Extending Patterns — page 56)

Judy looks for patterns to help her solve crimes.

Who helps her? To find out, extend each pattern. Then crack the code!

Letter Code

A ●   K ▲   D ●   I ▲
N ■   C ▲   S ■

N I C K
1 2 3 4

HINT Match each shape and number to a letter to crack the code.

56

Colour to Complete
(Creating Patterns — page 57)

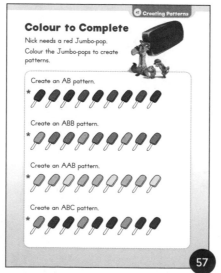

Nick needs a red Jumbo-pop. Colour the Jumbo-pops to create patterns.

Create an AB pattern.
*

Create an ABB pattern.
*

Create an AAB pattern.
*

Create an ABC pattern.
*

57

*Sample answers provided.

106

Fill In the Blanks

Identifying Pattern Rules

Moana leaves the secret cave feeling excited. Her ancestors sailed the open sea!

Circle each pattern core. Use words to describe the pattern core.

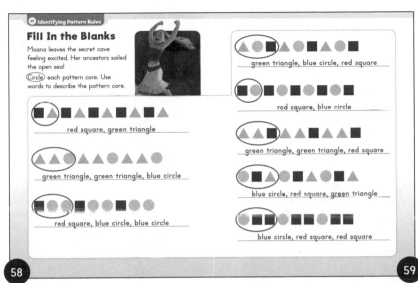

red square, green triangle

green triangle, green triangle, blue circle

red square, blue circle, blue circle

green triangle, blue circle, red square

red square, blue circle

green triangle, green triangle, red square

blue circle, red square, green triangle

blue circle, red square, red square

Identifying Missing Numbers

Fill In the Blanks

Emmitt Otterton is missing. But Judy is on the case! She wants to find all 14 missing mammals.

Determine the missing number in each equation. Use the space below each equation to show your work.

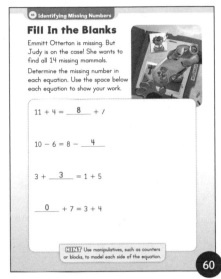

$11 + 4 = \underline{8} + 7$

$10 - 6 = 8 - \underline{4}$

$3 + \underline{3} = 1 + 5$

$\underline{0} + 7 = 3 + 4$

HINT Use manipulatives, such as counters or blocks, to model each side of the equation.

Identifying Missing Numbers

Fill In the Blanks

Chief Bogo is not impressed by the bag of stolen onions on his desk.

There are 11 onions. The mouldy onions are removed. 6 onions are left. How many mouldy onions are there?

To solve this problem, write it out like this: $11 - \underline{\quad} = 6$.

Determine each missing number. Use the blank space below each equation to show your work.

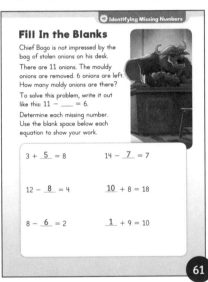

$3 + \underline{5} = 8$

$14 - \underline{7} = 7$

$12 - \underline{8} = 4$

$\underline{10} + 8 = 18$

$8 - \underline{6} = 2$

$\underline{1} + 9 = 10$

61

Identifying Greater Than and Less Than

Maze

Help Moana and Maui get away from Tamatoa. Follow the greater numbers.

Now, help Moana and Maui continue their journey. Follow the lesser numbers.

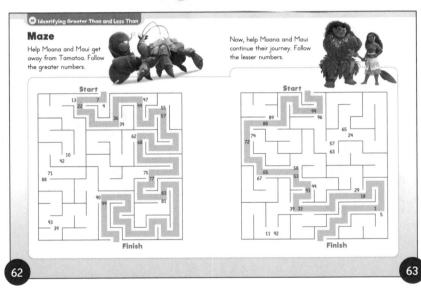

Start

Finish

Start

Finish

62 **63**

Understanding Patterns in Time

Out of Order

Judy's job as a meter maid is all about timing. She hands out parking tickets when time expires on the meter.

Number these parking tickets in order from earliest to latest. Write **1** beside the earliest ticket. Write **6** beside the latest ticket.

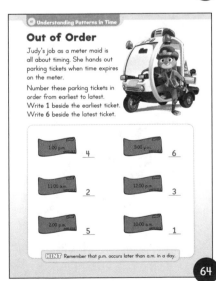

1:00 p.m. — 4

3:00 p.m. — 6

11:00 a.m. — 2

12:00 p.m. — 3

2:00 p.m. — 5

10:00 a.m. — 1

HINT Remember that p.m. occurs later than a.m. in a day.

64

Understanding Patterns in Time

Matching

Nick puts a lot of time into his hustles. His schedule is very organized.

Match each timed activity with the correct clock.

Meet Finnick at 10:30 a.m.

Go to Jumbeaux's Café at 10:45 a.m.

Melt the Jumbo-pop at 11:00 a.m.

Sell pawpsicles at 11:45 a.m.

Count the profits at 1:15 p.m.

65

*Sample answers provided.

Answers

Matching

Judy packs her favourite things into her suitcase when she moves to Zootopia. The length of a suitcase can be measured in centimetres.

Match each item to the most appropriate unit of measurement that should be used to determine length.

Match each item to the most appropriate unit of measurement that should be used to determine mass.

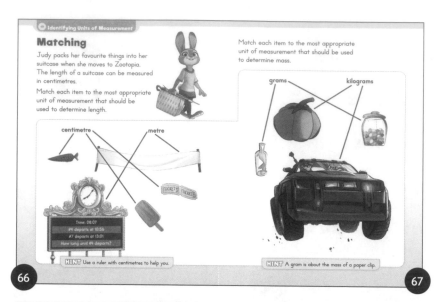

centimetre   metre

grams   kilograms

Time: 08:07
#4 departs at 10:56
#7 departs at 13:01
How long until #4 departs?

HINT Use a ruler with centimetres to help you.

HINT A gram is about the mass of a paper clip.

66   67

Fill In the Blanks

Moana uses her hand to measure the stars. You can also use your finger to measure things. Look at the width of your pointer finger.

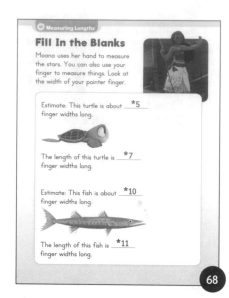

Estimate: This turtle is about __*5__ finger widths long.

The length of this turtle is __*7__ finger widths long.

Estimate: This fish is about __*10__ finger widths long.

The length of this fish is __*11__ finger widths long.

68

Out of Order

The villagers of Motunui play many different drums.

Look at the width of your pointer finger. Measure the height of each drum. Then order these drums by height from shortest to tallest.

__2__   __3__   __1__
__3__   __6__   __2__
finger widths   finger widths   finger widths

HINT Write 1 beside the shortest drum.
Write 3 beside the tallest drum.

69

Fill In the Blanks

Mr. and Mrs. Hopps are farmers. They plant carrots, potatoes, and kale in their garden.

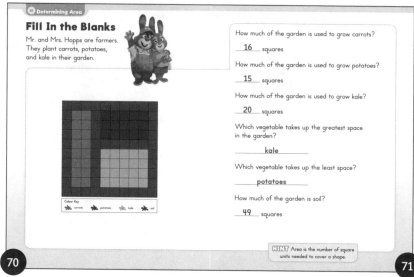

Colour Key
carrots   potatoes   kale   soil

How much of the garden is used to grow carrots?
__16__ squares

How much of the garden is used to grow potatoes?
__15__ squares

How much of the garden is used to grow kale?
__20__ squares

Which vegetable takes up the greatest space in the garden?
__kale__

Which vegetable takes up the least space?
__potatoes__

How much of the garden is soil?
__49__ squares

HINT Area is the number of square units needed to cover a shape.

70   71

Colour to Complete

Help the Hopps plan their garden for next year.

Colour the grid to show how you would plant the vegetables. Use the Colour Key. Each square represents one plant.

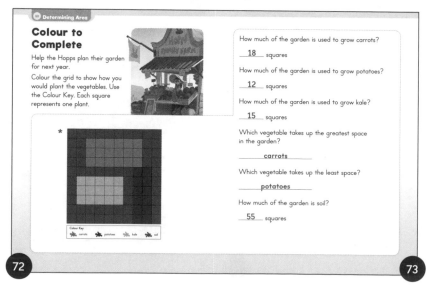

*

Colour Key
carrots   potatoes   kale   soil

How much of the garden is used to grow carrots?
__18__ squares

How much of the garden is used to grow potatoes?
__12__ squares

How much of the garden is used to grow kale?
__15__ squares

Which vegetable takes up the greatest space in the garden?
__carrots__

Which vegetable takes up the least space?
__potatoes__

How much of the garden is soil?
__55__ squares

72   73

Out of Order

Zootopia police officers are all very different.

Order the characters by mass from lightest to heaviest. Write 1 below the lightest character and 4 below the heaviest

__2__   __3__   __4__   __1__

74

*Sample answers provided.

108

Out of Order

Nick and Finnick fill empty water bottles with rainwater. They take the water bottles to Sahara Square and sell them.

Order the containers by capacity from least to greatest.

| 4 | 1 | 3 | 2 |

Fill In the Blanks

Moana washes up on shore after a storm. How do you prepare for stormy weather?

Use the words in the Word Bank to complete each sentence.

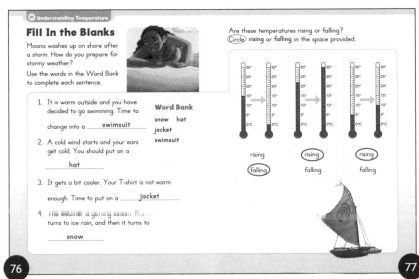

1. It is warm outside and you have decided to go swimming. Time to change into a ___swimsuit___

2. A cold wind starts and your ears get cold. You should put on a ___hat___

3. It gets a bit cooler. Your T-shirt is not warm enough. Time to put on a ___jacket___

4. The weather is getting colder. The rain turns to ice rain, and then it turns to ___snow___

Word Bank

snow   hat
jacket
swimsuit

Are these temperatures rising or falling?
(Circle) rising or falling in the space provided.

rising   (rising)   (rising)
(falling)   falling   falling

Matching

Judy has a busy day ahead of her! Determine the best time for Judy to do these activities.

Draw a line to match each activity to a time of day.

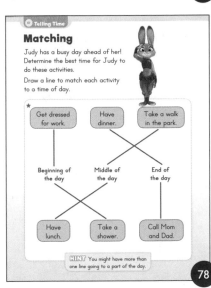

| Get dressed for work. | Have dinner. | Take a walk in the park. |

Beginning of the day   Middle of the day   End of the day

| Have lunch. | Take a shower. | Call Mom and Dad. |

HINT You might have more than one line going to a part of the day.

Fill In the Blanks

Judy loves her job! She uses a clock to get to work on time.

*Show what time you wake up for school.

7:30 AM/PM

Show what time you eat lunch.

11:30 AM/PM

Show what time you go to bed.

8:00 AM/PM

Matching

Judy's badge is a unique shape. Match each shape to its description.

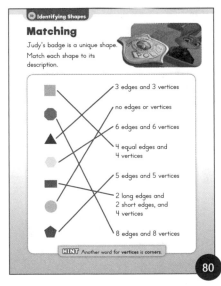

3 edges and 3 vertices

no edges or vertices

6 edges and 6 vertices

4 equal edges and 4 vertices

5 edges and 5 vertices

2 long edges and 2 short edges, and 4 vertices

8 edges and 8 vertices

HINT Another word for **vertices** is corners.

Picture Clues

Nick is looking out the window of the subway car. That window is shaped like a rectangle.

What other shapes do you see in this scene? Label some of the shapes you see.

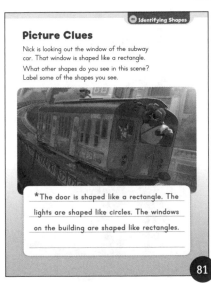

*The door is shaped like a rectangle. The lights are shaped like circles. The windows on the building are shaped like rectangles.

Colour to Complete

Gramma Tala tells the tale of Te Fiti to a group of village children. She is holding up 2 pictures that have 4 sides.

How many sides does each of these shapes have? Colour the shapes. Use the Colour Key.

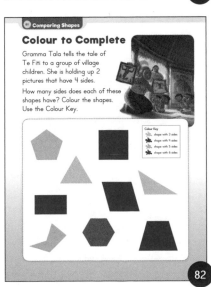

Colour Key
shape with 3 sides
shape with 4 sides
shape with 5 sides
shape with 6 sides

Matching

Moana finds boats in a cave. The sails on the boats have 3 sides.

Look at the shapes in each circle. Determine the sorting rule.

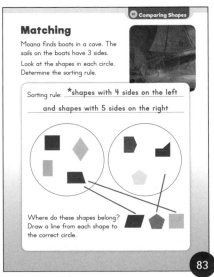

Sorting rule: *shapes with 4 sides on the left and shapes with 5 sides on the right

Where do these shapes belong? Draw a line from each shape to the correct circle.

---

75   76   77   78   79   80   81   82   83

Answers

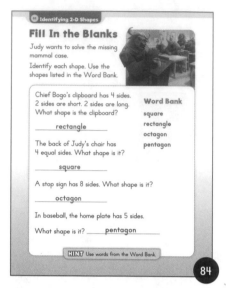

Identifying 2-D Shapes

Fill In the Blanks

Judy wants to solve the missing mammal case.

Identify each shape. Use the shapes listed in the Word Bank.

Chief Bogo's clipboard has 4 sides. 2 sides are short. 2 sides are long. What shape is the clipboard?

__rectangle__

The back of Judy's chair has 4 equal sides. What shape is it?

__square__

A stop sign has 8 sides. What shape is it?

__octagon__

In baseball, the home plate has 5 sides.

What shape is it? __pentagon__

Word Bank

square
rectangle
octagon
pentagon

HINT Use words from the Word Bank.

84

Identifying 2-D Shapes

Colour to Complete

Judy's shirt and Nick's tie have geometric patterns.

Colour the shapes to create a geometric design. Use the Colour Key.

Colour Key
hexagon   triangle   rhombus   square   pentagon

85

Identifying Symmetry

Matching

Pua is standing on a rock. The rock is symmetrical.

Make symmetrical shapes by matching the halves.

86

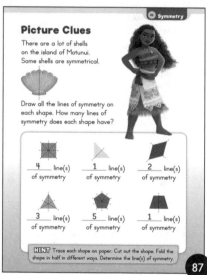

Symmetry

Picture Clues

There are a lot of shells on the island of Motunui. Some shells are symmetrical.

Draw all the lines of symmetry on each shape. How many lines of symmetry does each shape have?

__4__ line(s) of symmetry

__1__ line(s) of symmetry

__2__ line(s) of symmetry

__3__ line(s) of symmetry

__5__ line(s) of symmetry

__1__ line(s) of symmetry

HINT Trace each shape on paper. Cut out the shape. Fold the shape in half in different ways. Determine the line(s) of symmetry.

87

Identifying Prisms

Word Search

Duke Weaselton holds a bag shaped like a rectangular prism.

Find prism words in the word search.

VERTICES   SIDE   VERTEX
EDGE   FACE

```
O Z Z V F P A K
R Z G X Z D S Y
L T W O Z Y V Q
P V E R T E X P
F A W S I D E L
K H W Q F A C E
V E R T I C E S
P E D G E K A R
```

HINT As you look for a word, think about what it means.

88

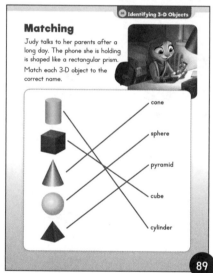

Identifying 3-D Objects

Matching

Judy talks to her parents after a long day. The phone she is holding is shaped like a rectangular prism.

Match each 3-D object to the correct name.

cone

sphere

pyramid

cube

cylinder

89

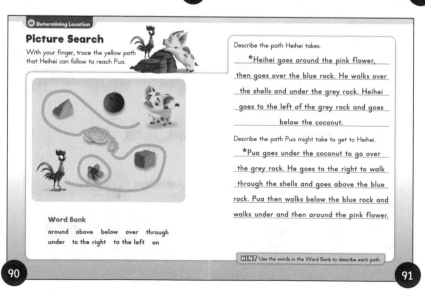

Determining Location

Picture Search

With your finger, trace the yellow path that Heihei can follow to reach Pua.

Word Bank

around   above   below   over   through
under   to the right   to the left   on

Describe the path Heihei takes.

*Heihei goes around the pink flower, then goes over the blue rock. He walks over the shells and under the grey rock. Heihei goes to the left of the grey rock and goes below the coconut.

Describe the path Pua might take to get to Heihei.

*Pua goes under the coconut to go over the grey rock. He goes to the right to walk through the shells and goes above the blue rock. Pua then walks below the blue rock and walks under and then around the pink flower.

HINT Use the words in the Word Bank to describe each path.

90

91

*Sample answers provided.

Picture Clues

Officer Clawhauser keeps a jar of candy on his desk. Imagine that the candies below are the only ones left in the jar.

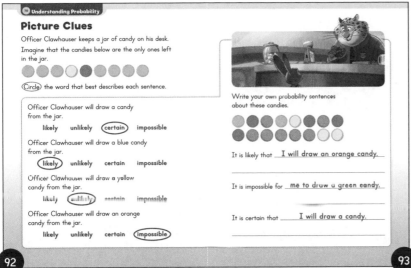

⊙ⒸⓄⓄⓄⓄⓄⓄⓄⓄ

(Circle) the word that best describes each sentence.

Officer Clawhauser will draw a candy from the jar.

likely   unlikely   (certain)   impossible

Officer Clawhauser will draw a blue candy from the jar.

(likely)   unlikely   certain   impossible

Officer Clawhauser will draw a yellow candy from the jar.

likely   (unlikely)   certain   impossible

Officer Clawhauser will draw an orange candy from the jar.

likely   unlikely   certain   (impossible)

Write your own probability sentences about these candies.

●●●●●●●●●●

It is likely that __I will draw an orange candy.__

_____

It is impossible for __me to draw a green candy.__

_____

It is certain that __I will draw a candy.__

_____

92   93

Picture Clues

Little Moana is collecting coconuts. She sees Heihei trip over a rock. How many rocks and coconuts are there? Take a tally to record the data.

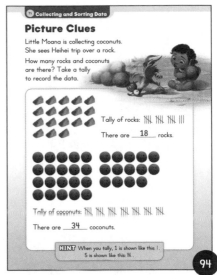

Tally of rocks: 𝍫 𝍫 𝍫 III

There are __18__ rocks.

Tally of coconuts: 𝍫 𝍫 𝍫 𝍫 𝍫 𝍫 IIII

There are __34__ coconuts.

HINT When you tally, 1 is shown like this: I.
5 is shown like this: 𝍫 .

94

Graphing

Little Moana and her friends draw pictures of things on the island. This tally chart shows the number of pictures they draw of each item.

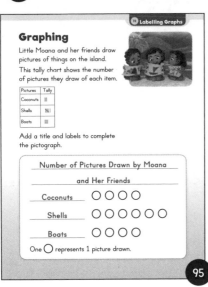

Pictures	Tally
Coconuts	III
Shells	𝍫 I
Boats	IIII

Add a title and labels to complete the pictograph.

Number of Pictures Drawn by Moana and Her Friends	
Coconuts	○ ○ ○ ○
Shells	○ ○ ○ ○ ○ ○
Boats	○ ○ ○ ○

One ○ represents 1 picture drawn.

95

Graphing

Customers at Jumbeaux's Café try different ice cream flavours. In one hour, Jumbeaux sells 6 chocolate cones, 5 vanilla cones, 8 strawberry cones, and 4 orange cones.

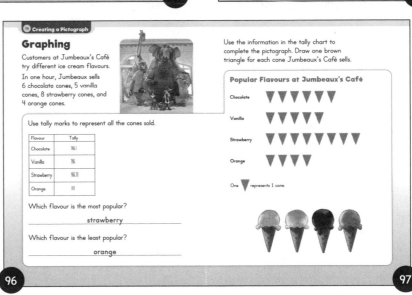

Use tally marks to represent all the cones sold.

Flavour	Tally
Chocolate	𝍫 I
Vanilla	𝍫
Strawberry	𝍫 III
Orange	IIII

Which flavour is the most popular?

__strawberry__

Which flavour is the least popular?

__orange__

Use the information in the tally chart to complete the pictograph. Draw one brown triangle for each cone Jumbeaux's Café sells.

Popular Flavours at Jumbeaux's Café

Chocolate   ▽ ▽ ▽ ▽ ▽ ▽

Vanilla   ▽ ▽ ▽ ▽ ▽

Strawberry   ▽ ▽ ▽ ▽ ▽ ▽ ▽ ▽

Orange   ▽ ▽ ▽ ▽

One ▼ represents 1 cone.

96   97

Graphing

Moana and Gramma Tala collect shells. How many shells of each colour are there?

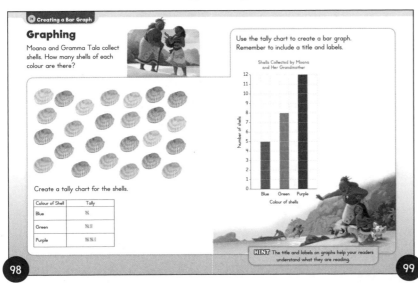

Create a tally chart for the shells.

Colour of Shell	Tally
Blue	𝍫
Green	𝍫 III
Purple	𝍫 𝍫 II

Use the tally chart to create a bar graph. Remember to include a title and labels.

Shells Collected by Moana and Her Grandmother

(bar graph: Blue = 5, Green = 8, Purple = 12)
Number of shells (y-axis 0–12)
Colour of shells (x-axis: Blue, Green, Purple)

HINT The title and labels on graphs help your readers understand what they are reading.

98   99

*Sample answers provided.

111

Learning Tools

1	2	3	4	5	6	7	8	9	10
11	12	13	14	15	16	17	18	19	20
21	22	23	24	25	26	27	28	29	30
31	32	33	34	35	36	37	38	39	40
41	42	43	44	45	46	47	48	49	50
51	52	53	54	55	56	57	58	59	60
61	62	63	64	65	66	67	68	69	70
71	72	73	74	75	76	77	78	79	80
81	82	83	84	85	86	87	88	89	90
91	92	93	94	95	96	97	98	99	100

Learning Tools

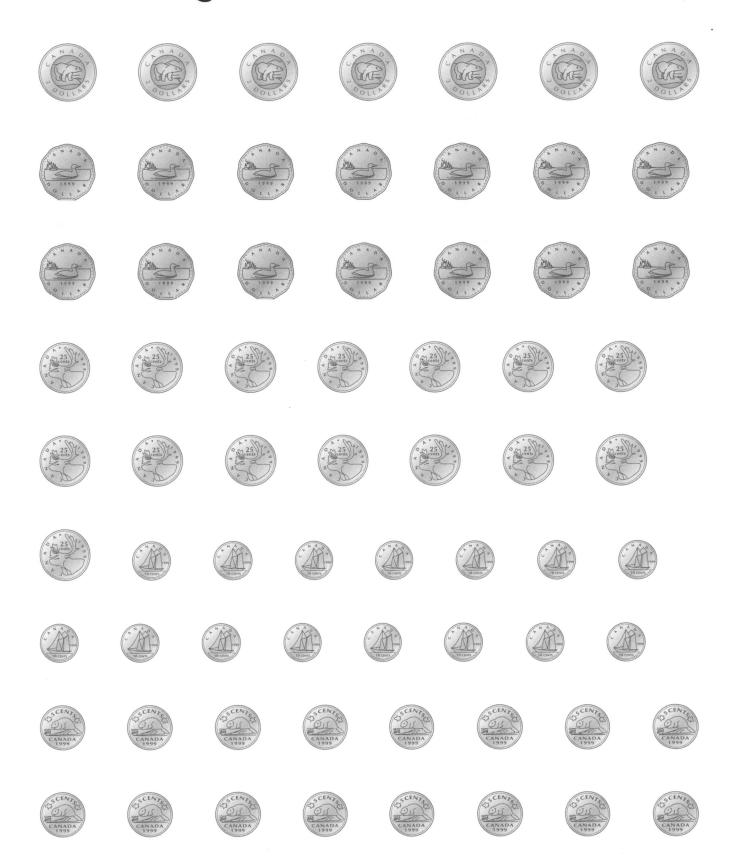

Learning Tools

13 + 13 ———	40 + 38 ———	22 + 22 ———
50	83	80
75 + 25 ———	81 + 10 ———	56 + 9 ———
64	62	50
83 − 81 ———	90 − 30 ———	75 − 50 ———
40	10	74

$$71 + 9$$

44

$$20 + 63$$

78

$$25 + 25$$

26

$$19 + 31$$

65

$$15 + 47$$

91

$$32 + 32$$

100

$$84 - 10$$

25

$$17 - 7$$

60

$$54 - 14$$

2

Cut out these flash cards. Use them to practise addition and subtraction.

Congratulations

_____ !

Print your name.

You have finished the
Brain Boost learning path.
Way to go!